Contents

Handwriting worktext 1

Third Edition

bju press®

Greenville, South Carolina

Note:
The fact that materials produced by other publishers may be referred to in this volume does not constitute an endorsement of the content or theological position of materials produced by such publishers. Any references and ancillary materials are listed as an aid to the student or the teacher and in an attempt to maintain the accepted academic standards of the publishing industry.

HANDWRITING 1 WORKTEXT **Third Edition**

Coordinating Author
L. Michelle Rosier

Authors
Christine W. Kuhr
Susan J. Lehman
Melodye W. Snyder

Project Editor
Elizabeth Bang Berg

Bible Integration
Bryan Smith
William L. Gray

Compositor
Jung Yon Kim

Cover and Book Designer
Aaron Dickey

Illustration Coordinator
Dave Schuppert

Project Manager
Dan Woodhullm

Illustrators
Julie Arsenault
Anne Bastine
Paula Cheadle
Cory Godbey

Preston Gravely
Jim Hargis
Caroline G. Lott
Kathy Pflug
Dave Schuppert
Lynda Slattery

© 2005, 2014 BJU Press
Greenville, South Carolina 29609

First Edition © 1987 BJU Press
Second Edition © 1998 BJU Press

ISBN 978-1-60682-812-0

15 14 13 12 11 10 9

Welcome to Handwriting 1!

Handwriting 1 will help you write words well. Others will be able to read what you write.

Learn to write each letter and number. Find out how to hold your pencil. Write a sentence about ducks. Enjoy a story about a sea horse.

How can you use what you learn? Write to tell others about God. Write to show love and to help others.

Get ready to write!

Letter to Parents

Dear Parent,

This year your child will use **_HANDWRITING 1 WORKTEXT_** Third Edition, which uses a unique style of writing developed by BJU Press. **_HANDWRITING 1 WORKTEXT_** seeks to lay a foundation of writing skills on which early learning is broadened and reinforced.

The program introduces the PreCursive alphabet at the kindergarten level and continues to provide meaningful PreCursive writing activities for first grade and the first ten weeks of second grade. Cursive is introduced in second grade and reinforced throughout the elementary grades.

PreCursive handwriting eliminates problems inherent in the formation of manuscript letters and provides an age-appropriate form of writing. Children use a natural slant, elliptical movements, and a smooth flow of writing. Most of the letters are made with one stroke, which eliminates midletter choices and reduces reversals. Letters look enough like the print students read that they can readily make a connection between reading and writing. Most students will find it easy to accomplish the transition from PreCursive to cursive.

The alphabet that your child is learning to recognize and write is included on the back of this page for your guidance. The arrows on the letters and numbers indicate the direction and order of the strokes. After letter formations have been taught at school, your child will benefit from additional guidance at home.

Thank you for your support and help at home.

Sincerely,

Grade 1 Teacher

PreCursive Alphabet

Aa Bb Cc Dd Ee Ff

Gg Hh Ii Jj Kk Ll Mm

Nn Oo Pp Qq Rr Ss Tt

Uu Vv Ww Xx Yy Zz

Numbers

0 1 2 3 4 5 6 7 8 9

  **T t letters**

Trace the letters.

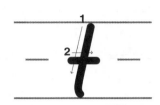

T
1. Drop.
2. Cross.

t
1. Drop and curve.
2. Cross.

Trace and write the letters.

T   T   T

t   t   t

Read and trace.

ten
ten

cat
cat

 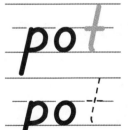

pot
pot

kit
kit

Trace and write.

I i letters

Trace the letters.

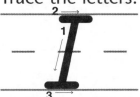

1. Drop.
2. Cross.
3. Cross.

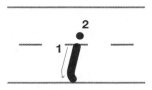

1. Drop and curve.
2. Dot.

Trace and write the letters.

Read and trace.

in
in

pin
pin

pit
pit

sit
sit

Trace and write.

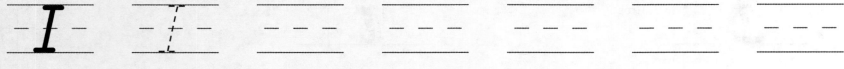

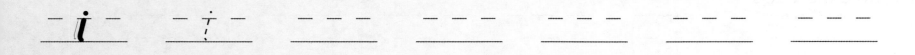

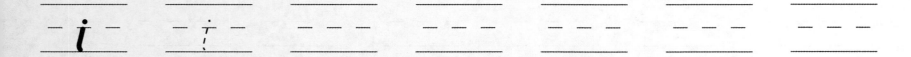

Extended Practice

 **S s** letters

Trace the letters.

 S

1. Begin near the top; swerve around and back.

s

1. Begin near the middle; swerve around and back.

Trace and write the letters.

S   S   S

s   s   s

Read and trace.

sin

sin

sad

sad

six

six

set

set

Trace and write.

S   S

S   S

s   s

s   s

is   is

 **letters**

Trace the letters.

 1. Drop, retrace, and swing right; drop and curve.

 1. Drop, retrace, and swing right; drop and curve.

Trace and write the letters.

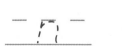

Read and trace.

net
net

pen
pen

tin
tin

nap
nap

Trace and write.

n

n

n

n

tin

Extended
Practice

 **Ww** letters

Trace the letters.

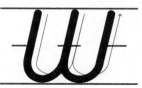 1. Drop and swing up; retrace and swing up.

 1. Drop and swing up; retrace and swing up.

Trace and write the letters.

Read and trace.

win

well

wet

wag

win

well

wet

wag

Trace and write.

w   w

w   w

w   w

w   w

win   win

**Extended
Practice**

Hh letters

Trace the letters.

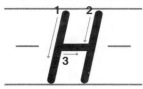

1. Drop.
2. Drop.
3. Cross.

1. Drop, retrace, and swing right; drop and curve.

Trace and write the letters.

H H H

h h h

Read and trace.

ham
ham

hat
hat

hen
hen

hand
hand

Trace and write.

H　H

H　H

h　h

h　h

his　his

Extended Practice

 **Dd** letters

Trace the letters.

 D

1. Drop; swing around and up to touch.

d

1. Begin near the middle; swing around and up; climb high; retrace and curve.

Trace and write the letters.

D D D

d d d

Read and trace.

dad

dad

dig

dig

dog

dog

lid

lid

© 2005 BJU Press. Reproduction prohibited.

Trace and write.

D   D

D   D

d   d

d   d

hid hid

Ee letters

Trace the letters.

1. Begin near the top; swing around to the middle; swing around again.

1. Swing up and around.

Trace and write the letters.

Read and trace.

b e d

r e d

n e s t

s e n d

Trace and write.

$\mathcal{E}$ $\mathcal{E}$

$\mathcal{E}$ $\mathcal{E}$

e e

e e

$\mathcal{E}d$ $\mathcal{E}d$

Extended Practice

Bb letters

Trace the letters.

 **B** 1. Drop, retrace, and swing around to touch; retrace and swing around to touch.

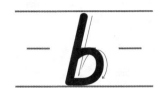 **b** 1. Drop, retrace to the middle, and swing around to touch.

Trace and write the letters.

 B   B   B

 b   b   b

Read and trace. Circle the word that matches the picture of the boy.

 hit

 hen

Ben

 bit

Ben

Trace and write.

B   B

B   B

b   b

b   b

web   web

Extended Practice

 **Uu** letters

Trace the letters.

1. Drop and swing up; retrace and curve.

1. Drop and swing up; retrace and curve.

Trace and write the letters.

Read and trace.

bus

bus

nut

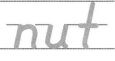

nut

sun

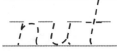

sun

sub

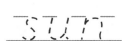

sub

Trace and write.

U   U

U   U

u   u

u   u

tub   tub

Extended Practice

 **letters**

Trace the letters.

 P

1. Drop, retrace, and swing around to touch.

 p

1. Drop low, retrace, and swing around to touch.

Trace and write the letters.

 P   P   P

P   P   P

Read and trace.

 lips

  man

 cup

 pup

lip   hip   cup   pup

lip   hip   cup   pup

Trace and write.

P   P

P   P

P   P

P   P

pen   pen

Extended Practice

Cc, Kk letters

Trace the letters.

1. Begin near the top and swing around.

1. Begin near the middle and swing around.

Trace and write the letters.

Trace the letters.

1. Drop.
2. Drop left; then right and curve.

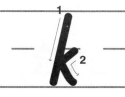

1. Drop.
2. Drop left; then right and curve.

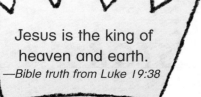

Jesus is the king of heaven and earth.
—*Bible truth from Luke 19:38*

Trace and write the letters.

Trace and write.

C   C

c   c

K   K

k   k

sick   sick

Extended Practice

 **Aa** letters

Trace the letters.

 A
1. Drop left.
2. Drop right.
3. Cross.

a
1. Begin near the middle; swing around to touch; retrace and curve.

Trace and write the letters.

 A A A

 a a a

Read and trace.

2
+ 2
4

add

 SODA

can

cap

sack

 add can cap sack

Trace and write.

A A A

A A A

a a a

a a a

sad sad

Mark It

Trace the question mark.

1. Begin near the top; swing around and down.
2. Dot.

Trace and write the question mark.

Read and trace the question.

What is it?

Read, trace, and write.

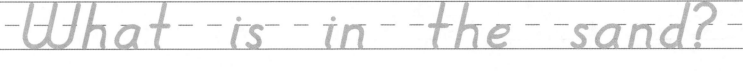

sand   *sand*

Trace and write.

Tt Ii Ss Ww Nn

Hh Ee Bb Pp Uu

Kk Cc Dd Aa

Extended Practice

Ll letters

Trace the letters.

 L   1. Drop; glide right.

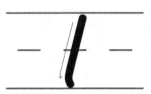 l   1. Drop and curve.

Jesus is the Lamb of God.
—*Bible truth from John 1:29*

Trace and write the letters.

 L

 l

Read and trace.

bell

bell

sell

sell

tell

tell

hill

hill

Trace and write.

L   L

L   L

l   l

l   l

land   land

Extended Practice

 **Gg letters**

Trace the letters.

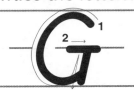

1. Begin near the top; swing around to the middle and drop.
2. Cross.

1. Begin near the middle; swing around to touch; drop low and hook.

Trace and write the letters.

Read and trace.

pig
pig

leg
leg

bug
bug

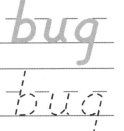

bag
bag

Trace and write.

G   G

G   G

g   g

g   g

wag   wag

Extended Practice

Review n, t

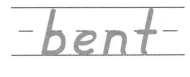

Read and trace the words.

bent   sent   ant

bent   sent   ant

Trace and write the letters.

dent   went   pant

dent   went   pant

Read, trace, and write.

Did the ants pant?

Did

Trace and write.

nt   nt

nt   nt

tent   tent

dent   dent

Dad went in the tent.

Extended Practice

M m letters

Trace the letters.

1. Drop, retrace, and swing right; drop, retrace, and swing right; drop and curve.

1. Drop, retrace, and swing right; drop, retrace, and swing right; drop and curve.

Trace and write the letters.

m   m   m

m   m   m

Read and trace.

ham

him

mug

mend

ham

him

mug

mend

Trace and write.

m   m

m   m

m   m

m   m

hum   hum

Extended Practice

 **letters**

Trace the letters.

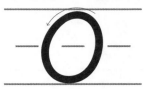 1. Begin near the top; swing around to touch.

 1. Begin near the middle; swing around to touch.

Trace and write the letters.

Read and trace. Match the words with the pictures.

sock

cot

doll

Mom

Trace and write.

Tom is on the dock.

Extended Practice

0, 1, 2 numbers

Trace the numbers.

 0

1. Begin near the top; swing around to touch.

 1

1. Drop.

 2

1. Begin near the top; swing right and down to the left; glide right.

Trace and write the numbers.

 0   0   0    0   0   0   0    0

1   1   1

 2   2   2

How many? Trace the numbers and words.

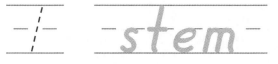 0 logs   1 stem   2 steps

Trace and write.

0   0

1   1

2   2

Stan sat still.

3, 4, 5 numbers

Trace the numbers.

3
1. Begin near the top; swing around to the middle; swing around again.

4
1. Drop to the middle and glide right.
2. Drop.

5
1. Drop to the middle and swing around.
2. Glide right.

Trace and write the numbers.

  3

  4

  5

Read and trace.

   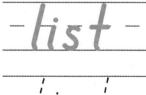

rest   dust   last   list

rest   dust   last   list

Trace and write.

3　3

3　3

4　4

4　4

5　5

5　5

**Extended
Practice**

Rr letters

Trace the letters.

R

1. Drop, retrace, and swing around to touch; drop right and curve.

r

1. Drop, retrace, and swing right.

Trace and write the letters.

R   R   R   _   _   _

r   r   r   _   _   _

Read and trace.

rip
rip

ran
ran

rat
rat

rod
rod

Trace and write.

R   R

R   R

r   r

r   r

What did Rick rip?

Vv letters

Trace the letters.

 1. Drop right; climb right.

1. Drop right; climb right.

Trace and write the letters.

Read and trace.

van

van

vat

vat

vet

vet

vest

vest

Trace and write.

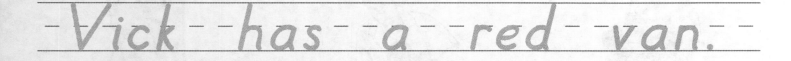

Vick has a red van.

Trace the letters.

1. Drop.
2. Glide right.
3. Glide right.

1. Begin near the top; swing around and drop low.
2. Cross.

Trace and write the letters.

  F   F   F

  f   f   f

Read and trace the words.

gift
gift

lift
lift

sift
sift

Read, trace, and write.

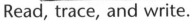

puff

stuff

Trace and write.

Sam has one gift.

Extended Practice

6, 7 numbers

Trace the numbers.

6
1. Begin near the top; swing down and around to touch.

7
1. Glide right; drop left.

Trace and write the numbers.

6   6   6

7   7   7

Count and trace.

6   gifts

6   gifts

7   pots

7   pots

Trace and write.

6　　6

6　　6

7　　7

7　　7

6　pigs　　7　legs

Extended Practice

 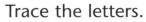
Trace the letters.

J

1. Drop and hook.

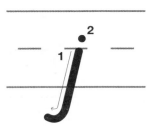

j

1. Drop low and hook.
2. Dot.

Jesus is the Son of God.
—*Bible truth from John 20:31*

Trace and write the letters.

J   J   J

j   j   j

Read and trace.

jump
jump

hump
hump

dump
dump

stump
stump

Trace and write.

J J

J J

j j

j j

jug jug

Extended Practice

Trace the letters.

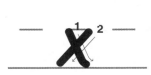

1. Drop right and curve.
2. Drop left.

1. Drop right and curve.
2. Drop left.

Trace and write the letters.

Read and trace.

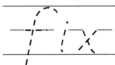

fix

fix

ax

ax

fox

fox

mixer

mixer

Trace and write.

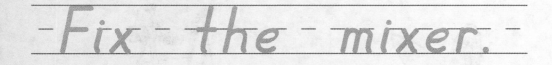

Fix the mixer.

 **Yy, Zz letters**

Trace the letters.

1. Drop and swing up; retrace; drop and hook.

1. Drop and swing up; retrace; drop low and hook.

Trace and write the letters.

Trace the letters.

1. Glide right; drop left; glide right.

1. Glide right; drop left; glide right.

Trace and write the letters.

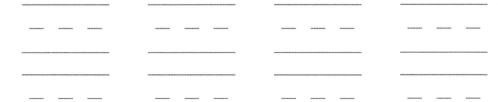

Trace and write.

y   y

y   y

Z   Z

z   z

yip   zip

Extended Practice

  **Qq letters**

Trace the letters.

1. Begin near the top; swing around to touch.
2. Slash and curve.

1. Begin near the middle; swing around to touch; drop low and crook.

Trace and write the letters.

Read and trace.

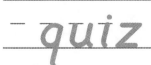

quack

quack

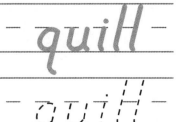

quiz

quiz

quill

quill

quick

quick

 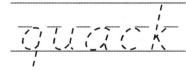

Trace and write.

  Q

Q

 q

q

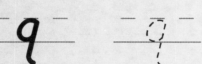 Will a duck quack?

Extended Practice

 **8, 9 numbers**

Trace the numbers.

 8

1. Begin near the top; swerve around and back; then up and around to touch.

 9

1. Begin near the top; swing around to touch; drop.

Trace and write the numbers.

 8   8   8

 9   9   9

Count, trace, and write.

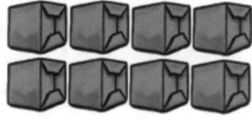

8   boxes

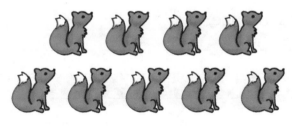

9   foxes

Trace and write.

Read, trace, and write the sentence.

A mixer mixes.

A New Belt

Read and write the sentence.

Max has a black belt.

Max

Read and write the words.

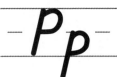   

milk   wept   elk   melt   help

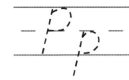

Write the letters.

Pp   Pp

Write the letters and words.

Aa

Ee

Ii

Oo

Uu

silk   felt

More Time for Review

Write the letters.

Gg   Bb   Mm   Dd   Vv   Ff

Gg

Rr   Jj   Xx   Zz   Yy   Qq

Read and write the sentence.

Glen will get a clam.

Glen

Write the letters.

Ll   *Ll*

Read and write the words.

clip

clop

flip

flop

fluff

plop

Trust the Lord

Read and write the words.

grip   drip   trip

grip

Read and write the sentence.

God wants us to

God

love and trust Him.

—Bible truth from Deuteronomy 6:5 and Proverbs 3:5

Write the letters.

Rr   Rr

Read and write the words.

crab

crib

drag

trap

trot

drift

Sniff, Sniff

Read and write the words.

snack   strap   crust   mask

snack

Read and write the sentences.

Sniff.   Sniff.

Can you smell the pig?

_ _ _ _ _ _ _ _ _ _ _ _ _ _ _ _ _ _ _ _

_____

Write the letters.

Ss   Ss

Read and write the words and sentence.

rust

trust

ask

task

Stan is stuck.

Extended Practice

Fishers of Men

Read and write the words.

fish

ship

shrimp

shell

fish

Read and write the sentence.

Will you tell of God's love?

Will

Write the letters.

Hh   *Hh*

Read and write the words and sentence.

cash

rash

dash

The cash is in the dish.

Extended Practice

Splash, Splash

Read and write the words.

crashes   dishes   rushes

crashes

flashes   wishes   crushes

Read and write the sentence.

Jed splashes in the tub.

Jed

Write the letters.

Ee Ee

Read and write the words and sentences.

clashes

flushes

brushes

Crash! The dishes fell.

The Chimps

Read and write the sentences.

Champ checks his chin.

Champ

Chubs munches his lunch.

A chimp is on the branch.

Write the letters.

Cc   Cc   - - -   - - -   - - -

Read and write the words.

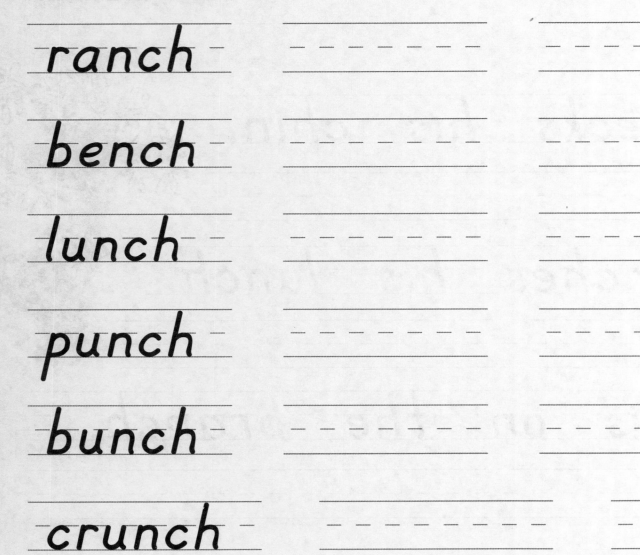

ranch

bench

lunch

punch

bunch

crunch

Extended Practice

Sing in the Spring

Read and write the sentence.

The finch sings in spring.

The

Read and write the words. Circle the three words that go with birds.

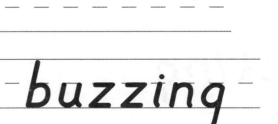

string

string

wing

singer

stinger

sang

buzzing

Write the letters.

Aa   *Aa*

Read and write the words.

bang

hang

pecking

bucking

quacking

grunting

Extended Practice

A Drink at the Sink

Read and write the words.

sink   *sank*   *drink*   *drank*

sink

Read and write the sentences.

A chipmunk is at the sink.

A

It is drinking.

Write the letters.

Kk   *Kk*

Read and write the words and sentence.

pink

blink

bank

crank

Mom has a pink drink.

Extended Practice

Be Thankful

Read and write the words.

thank
thank

think

math

path

Read and write the sentence.

God wants us to thank Him.

God

—Bible truth from Psalm 100:4

Write the letters.

Tt *Tt*

Read and write the words.

bath

with

thin

thick

thud

thump

Extended
Practice

A White Shell

Read and write the words.

whip   whip

whack

Read and write the sentences.

Seth has a shell.

Seth

It is a white shell.

Write the letters.

Ww   Ww

Read and write the words and sentence.

what

when

which

whiz

Clap your hands.

Extended Practice

That Yellow Zipper

_____

Read and write the words. Match the words with the pictures.

zipper

zipper

slipper

dinner

spinner

Read and write the sentence.

That zipper is yellow.

That

Write the letters.

Zz   Zz

Read and write the words.

hot

hotter

slim

slimmer

banner

scatter

Extended Practice

Sledding Fun

Read and write the words. Match the *–ing* words with the pictures.

trotted

trotted

trotting

trotting

batted

sledding

sledded

batting

Write the letters.

Dd   *Dd*

Read and write the words.

spot

spotted

pat

patting

plug

plugging

Extended Practice

Review Time

Read and write the words.

whisker   thinker

whisker

chipmunk   shelter

Read and write the sentence.

Chipmunks have whiskers.

Chipmunks

Read and write the words and sentence.

what

thing

chest

shrub

The chimp sat.

Extended
Practice

A Piper-Cub Flight

Read and write the words. Circle the things a pilot might take to a missionary.

 pans

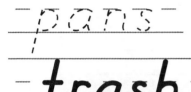 pans

Bibles

nest

trash

pots

quilts

Read and write the sentence.

Mr. Skinner has Bibles.

Mr.

Read and write the words.

cups

lamps

mixer

boxes

trunk

hammer

The Cat and the Fiddle

Read and write the words.

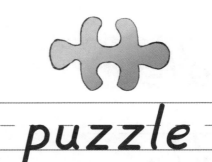

fiddle
freckles
puzzle

fiddle

goggles
bundle
ruffle

Write the letters.

Ff

Read and write the words and sentence.

apple

puddle

battle

cattle

Bring the king a pen.

Extended Practice

A Big Tumble

Read and write the sentences.

The pig had a

The

stumble. It led

to a big tumble.

Write the letters.

Gg Gg

Read and write the words.

big giggle

hot handle

little bubble

brown saddle

wet paddle

red rattle

Extended Practice

Camped Out

Read and write the words.

camped

camped

fished

chopped

thumped

hissed

docked

Read and write the word.

snapped

snapped

Read and write the words and sentence.

ask

asked

drop

dropped

The fish went splash!

Buzzed and Winked

Read and write the sentence.

One duck splashed.

One

Read and write the words.

buzzed

quacked

winked

buzzed

Write the letters.

Bb Bb

Read and write the words and sentence.

blinked

dipped

hummed

nibbled

The insect buzzed.

Extended Practice

Vowel Review

Write the letters.

Aa   *Ee*   *Ii*   *Oo*   *Uu*

Aa

Write the words.

cat   *elk*   *chick*   *fox*   *pup*

cat

Read and write the sentence.

Uncle Tom picked apples.

Uncle

Read and write the words and sentence.

eggs

milk

crop

bug

pig

hen

The hog sat in the mud.

Splash and Scatter

Read and write the sentences.

Otters were swimming.

Otters

Water splashes.

The fish scatter.

Splash!

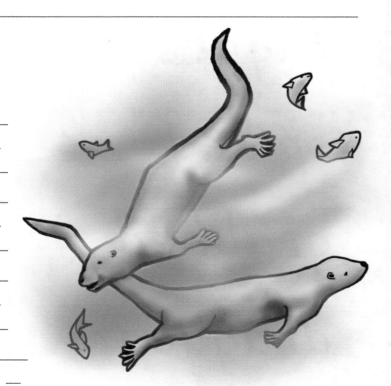

Read and write the words.

sobbed

hugged

tugged

spilled

grabbed

dragged

Extended Practice

Rushed and Yelled

Read and write the sentences.

The cattle rushed and

The

everyone yelled!

Skunks ran.

Write the numbers.

1 1

2 2

Read and write the words and sentence.

was

were

want

have

Mom said to run fast.

Names

Read and write the names.

Dave   Wade   Abe

Dave (trace)

Jane   James   Dale

Pencil

Write the sentence.

His name is Rex.

His (trace)

Write the letters.

Aa   _Aa_ (trace)

Read and write the words and sentence.

bake

cake

game

gave

Jake wades in the lake.

Extended Practice

Ride a Mile

Read and write the words.

dime   bike   fire   prize

dime

mile   like   wire   smile

Read and write the question.

Can you ride a bike?

Can

Write the letters.

Ii   Ii

Read and write the words and sentence.

dike

hike

lime

time

The tire was flat.

Extended
Practice

Buddy's Bone

Read and write the words.

cone   stove   globe   rope

_____   _____   _____   _____

cone   _____   _____   _____

Read and write the sentence.

Buddy has a bone.

_Buddy_____

_____

Write the letters.

Oo   Oo   _____   _____   _____

Read and write the words and sentence.

hole

nose

rose

poke

Sam kicked the stone.

Extended Practice

A Cute Flute

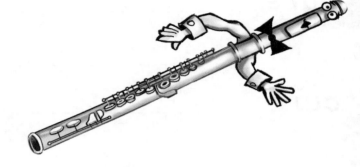

Read and write the phrase.

a cute flute

a

Read and write the words.

tune

tune

rule

fume

cube

June

mule

tube

plume

Write the letters.

Uu

Uu

Read and write the words and sentence.

pure

cure

duke

Luke

Dave sang a tune.

Extended Practice

Family Likes

Read and write the words.

cake

cake

game

campfire

smile

Read and write the sentence.

That family likes

That

to hike.

Read and write the words and sentence.

came

gave

five

wife

Alex gave Mom a gift.

What Are They?

Read and write the sentences.

Jack is a baker.

Jack

Jon is a skater.

Jake is a diver.

Jill is a rider.

Write the letters.

Jj   *Jj*

Read and write the words and sentence.

used

ruled

poked

glided

The dog came home.

Extended Practice

A Mole in a Hole

Read and write the words.

| broke | hose | mole | cube |

broke

| smoke | nose | pole | tube |

Read and write the sentence.

A mole is in a hole.

A

Write the number.

3   3

Read and write the sentences.

Dan ate a prune in June.

_____

- - - - - - - - - - - - - - - - -

_____

Do mules have rules?

_____

- - - - - - - - - - - - - - - - -

_____

Do not poke at the spoke.

_____

- - - - - - - - - - - - - - - - -

_____

Pulled and Tugged

Read and write the sentences.

Mike pulled the rope.

Mike

Then Mike tugged and tugged.

The mule sat still.

Write the numbers.

Read and write the words and sentence.

woke

yoke

tune

dune

The pinecone fell.

Trains and Rails

Read and write the sentence.

The train went off the rails.

The

Read and write the words.

rail   sail   rain   gain

rail

quail   mail   train   drain

Write the letters.

Qq   *Qq*

Read and write the words.

tail

frail

stain

nail

fail

pain

jail

snail

brain

pail

trail

drain

God's Day

Read and write the words. Draw lines to match the words with the pictures.

Sunday
Sunday

driveway
- - - - - - - - -

runway

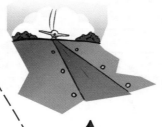

subway

stingray

haystack

Write the sentence.

Sunday is God's day.

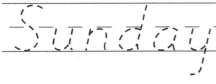
Sunday

Read and write the sentences.

The plane is not up.

It is still on the runway.

It cannot take off.

Cain will fix the plane.

Eve and Steve

Read and write the sentences.

Here is Eve.

Here

Here is Steve.

Read and write the sentence.

Eve and Steve are with me.

Eve

Write the letters.

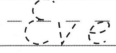 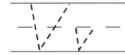

Read and write the words and sentence.

he

we

me

she

began

begin

It began to rain.

Extended Practice

A Peek at the Peak

Read and write the words.

heal

heel

weak

week

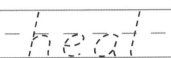

read

reed

peak

peek

Write the letters.

Mm

Read and write the words.

sheep

bleating

beetle

beeping

seagull

screeching

Full of Cheer

Read and write the sentences.

Jesus forgives sins.

Jesus

We will be full of cheer.

—Bible truth from Matthew 9:2

Read and write the words.

beaming zeal

beaming zeal

baking sweets

gleaming glee

lasting treat

Read and write the words and sentence.

meat _____   _____

meals _____   _____

needs _____   _____

sleep _____   _____

The teacher began to teach.

_____

Extended Practice

A Clean Sweep

Read and write the phrases.

wiping   the   glass

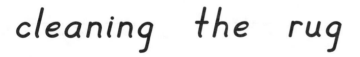

dipping   the   mop

sweeping   the   floor

cleaning   the   rug

Write the numbers.

Read and write the words and sentence.

cranked

squeaked

squealed

screamed

The hogs squealed

at the snake.

On a Ship

Read and write the sentences.

Last week we

~~Last~~

got on a ship.

We went on the sea.

Mom and I liked the waves.

Read and write the phrases.

bumpy street

_____

choppy sea

_____

creamy butter

_____

muddy water

_____

rainy day

_____

stuffy nose

_____

Extended Practice

Benny's Money

Read and write the sentences.

Benny has money.

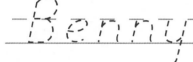

Will he get a funny bunny?

Will he get a peppy puppy?

Write the numbers.

Read and write the words and sentence.

silly

puffy

floppy

snappy

Is it a spunky puppy?

Snails in Streams

Read the words. Write them below the correct pictures.

snail
stream

stream

beaver
beehive

peacock
peanut

Read and write the sentence.

Some snails live in streams.

Some

Read and write the words and sentence.

hail

mail

team

dream

Can you see a pin

in a haystack?

Extended Practice

Pleasing God

Read and write the sentences.

Max will not lie.

Max

He seeks to please God.

—Bible truth from Colossians 3:9–10

Read and write the words.

pie   **lie**   **die**   **tie**

pie

Write the letters.

Read and write the words and sentence.

died

tied

dizzy

frizzy

Benny played leapfrog.

Extended Practice

A Shy Spy

Read and write the phrases.

shy fly

shy

shy spy

dry sky

sly fly

Read and write the sentence.

Why did the shy

Why

spy try to fly?

Read and write the words and sentence.

cry

crying

drying

flying

My kitty is fluffy.

Extended Practice

Peach Pie

Read and write the sentences.

Jimmy likes to

Jimmy

eat peach pie.

Whipped cream is yummy.

Write the number.

10   10

Read and write the words and sentence.

jacket

pocket

necktie

The butterfly is

flying by the plants.

Lights

Read and write the words.

light

flashlight

skylight

light (traced)

sunlight

lightning

spotlight

Read and write the sentence.

My plane flight is tonight.

My (traced)

Read and write the words and sentence.

night

fright

tonight

midnight

My flashlight is blue.

The Highway

Read and write the sentences.

Tonight we must drive on

Tonight

the highway.

It is raining and lightning.

We pray God keeps us safe.

—Bible truth from Psalm 56:3

Read and write the words and sentence.

visit

visiting

bright

brighten

The children prayed.

Boats

Read and write the words.

speedboat

steamboat

sailboat

speedboat

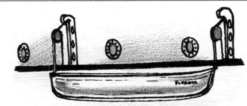

whaleboat

lifeboat

Read and write the sentence.

Joan can sail the sailboat.

Joan

Read and write the phrases.

boating buddy

groaning goat

soaking singer

floating foam

gripping goal

croaking cub

**Extended
Practice**

A Snowy Day

Read and write the words.

blow   blown   snow   snowing

blow

Read and write the sentences.

It is a snowy day.

It

Can you make a snowman?

Write the question mark.

? ?

Read and write the words.

mow

low

row

follow

window

pillow

Write the question mark.

 ?

A Rainbow

Read and write the words. Match the words with the pictures.

rainbow

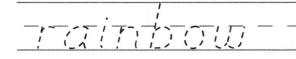

rowboat

_____

snowflake

_____

_____

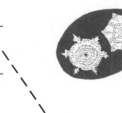

windowpane

_____

_____

Read and write the sentence.

Did you see the rainbow?

Did _____

Write the numbers.

 2   3 _____ 4 _____ 5 _____

Read and write the words and sentence.

flow

flown

grown

rowing

blowing

showing

Can you blow a bubble?

A Rowboat

Read and write the sentences.

Today   is   Friday.

Today

The   sun   is   shining.

Get   in   the   rowboat.

It   is   a   fine   boating   day.

Write the numbers.

6   *6*   7   8   9

Read and write the phrases.

croaking toad

rowing to land

following the highway

blowing on the windows

A Crow and a Doe

Read and write the words.

go

toe

snow

low

Read and write the sentences.

A crow is flying low.

A doe played in

the snow.

Read and write the words and sentence.

open

over

overflow

overgrown

overrun

oversleep

Please wash your hands.

Extended Practice

Blue

Read and write the words.

bluebell

bluefish

blue jeans

bluebell

Read and write the sentence.

Mr. True painted

Mr.

in his blue jeans.

Read and write the words and sentence.

Sue   clue   glue   true

cue   due   Tuesday

Sue made a snowman

on Tuesday.

Extended Practice

A Pet Beagle

Read and write the words.

eagle

table

ladle

bugle

eagle

Read and write the sentences.

I have a beagle.

I

Do you have a pet?

Read and write the words and sentence.

cable

noble

title

great

greater

greatest

A ladle fell off

the table.

Like Sheep

Read and write the sentences.

We are like sheep.

_We_

We do what we want to do.

We are sinners.

Jesus takes away sin.

—Bible truth from Isaiah 53:6

Write the letters.

g   g   g   g

Read and write the words and sentence.

baby

lady

bony

cozy

duty

holy

tidy

tiny

Judy likes meat and gravy.

A Holy God

Read and write the sentence.

The Bible tells us

The

that God is holy.

—Bible truth from Isaiah 6:3

Read and write the words.

Bible   watch   over   overcoat

Bible

Write the letters.

a   a   d   d

Read and write the words and sentence.

road table shiny cable

buzzed ladybug

The tiny ladybug landed

on the table.

Extended Practice

Skating in the City

Read and write the words.

cent   cider   cyclone

cent

Read and write the sentence.

A skating rink is

_A_

in the center of the city.

Read and trace the word.
Find the word in the sentence above with the same meaning.
Circle the word. Write the word on the blank line.

middle   _middle_

Read and write the words and sentence.

cell

cypress

cinder

boast

roast

toast

Can you coast

on your bike?

A Spaceship

Read and write the words. Draw lines to match the words with the pictures.

space

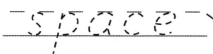

face

----

mice

price

Read and write the sentence.

A spaceship zips into space.

_A_ ----------

Write the letters.

 s   s   e    e

Read and write the words and sentence.

Nancy

lace

race

brace

grace

place

What is the

price for ice?

Carlos Camped

Read and write the sentence.

Carlos camped in a camper.

Carlos

Read and write the words below the correct picture.

| cake | cube | camp | cup |
| cot | cat | coat | cape |

cot

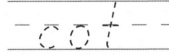

Read and write the words and sentence.

cable

coat

creep

croak

cozy

cute

Will you clean the coat?

Extended Practice

Cry or Weep

Read and write the synonyms.

cry  weep

ship  boat

_ _cry_ _

Read and write the sentences.

I love You, God.

_ _I_ _

God hears me when I cry.

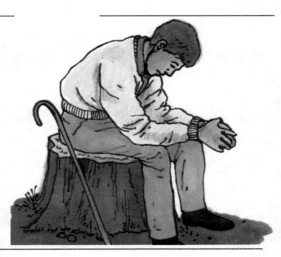

—Bible truth from Psalm 116:1–2, 8

Read and trace the word.
Find the word in the sentence above with the same meaning.
Circle the word. Write the word on the blank line.

weep _ _weep_ _

Read and write the words and sentence.

twice

penny

neat

tiny

clue

hint

trip

tumble

Your desk is neat and tidy.

Extended Practice

On the Farm

Read and write the words on the lines next to each hat.

bar
car
star

bar

arm
farm
charm

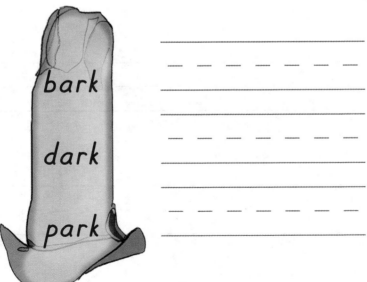

bark
dark
park

art
dart
start

Read and write the sentences.

Star is at

the T-Bar Ranch.

A star is

on his face.

The star is white.

Bart, Clark, and Mark

Read and write the sentences.

Bart can't park the cart.

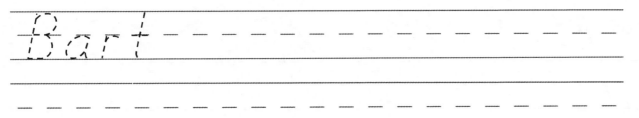

Clark didn't harm the tart.

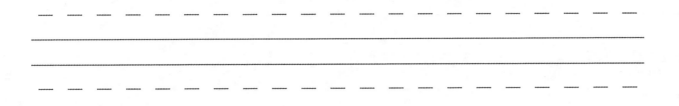

Mark isn't in the marsh.

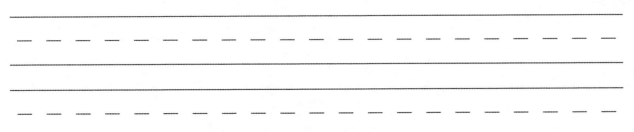

Read and write the sentences.

There's the barnyard.

Bart doesn't want the pig

to go into the garden.

Jan didn't lock the gate.

It ran into the garden.

At the Store

Read and write the sentence. Then read and write what Carl bought at the store.

GENERAL STORE

Carl rode his horse

Carl

to the store.

scarf

scarf

cornmeal

popcorn

pork

tarts

corn

Read and write the words and sentence.

born   horn   thorn   worn

core   sore   chore   shore

It is right to eat

pork with a fork.

Sea Horses

Read and write the sentences.

Some sea horses live

Some

in the tall sea grass.

They swim upright

in the water.

Have you seen a sea horse?

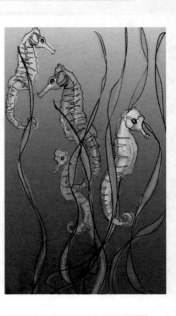

Read and write the words and sentence.

seashore

shoreline

starfish

seagull

Today there are not

many sea horses.

To Obey

Read and write the sentence.

The Bible tells children

The

to obey Mom and Dad.

—Bible truth from Ephesians 6:1

Read and write the words.

arch

arch

snore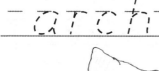

target

torch

cartwheel

stork

Read and write the words and sentence.

short

shorter

shortest

sharp

sharper

sharpest

smart

smarter

smartest

Have you ever seen a

stork in a snowstorm?

The Herd

Read and write the words.

herd   herder

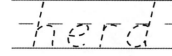

cattle   horses

Read and write the sentence.

Bert led the herd.

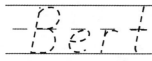

Write the letters.

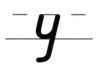 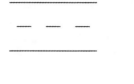 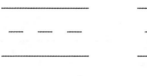

Read and write the words and sentences.

serve   storm   march

_____   _____   _____

— — — — — — —   — — — — — — —   — — — — — — —

_____   _____   _____

serving   storming   marching

_____   _____   _____

— — — — — — —   — — — — — — —   — — — — — — —

_____   _____   _____

It was a rainy day.

_____

— —

_____

Carl went into the barn.

_____

— —

_____

He did chores inside.

_____

— —

_____

186   Extended
      Practice

Not Hurt

Read and write the sentences. Circle the two *ur* words.

(Curt) fell off.

He didn't get hurt,

but a heel came off.

Write the letters.

i   *i*

l   *l*

Read and write the words and sentences.

burn

turn

hurt

burning

turning

spurt

A turkey cannot purr.

A turtle cannot hurdle.

Birds

Read and write the names of the birds.

hummingbird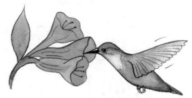

catbird

bluebird

blackbird

Read and write the sentence.

God made birds

on the fifth day.

—Bible truth from Genesis 1:21–23

Read and write the words and sentences.

chirp   dirt   girl

_____   _____   _____

- - - - - - - -   - - - - - - - -   - - - - - - - -

_____   _____   _____

chirped   shirt   swirl

_____   _____   _____

- - - - - - - -   - - - - - - - -   - - - - - - - -

_____   _____   _____

The girls put seeds

_____

- -

_____

in the bird feeder.

_____

- -

_____

The hungry birds chirped.

_____

- -

_____

Extended Practice

Hay Day

Read and write the words in the correct spaces.

or

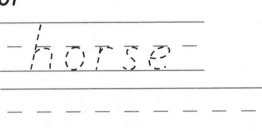

horse

er

ar

ir

ur

barn   turn
church bird
horse   store
farm   herd
verse   first

Write the letters.

t   t

f   f

Read and write the sentences.

Curt rode the horse

into the barn to rest.

The herd of cattle

wanted to eat oats.

They drank water.

Mark and Star

Read and write the sentences.

Mark rode Star to the

Mark

store. He got something

for them to eat. Mark

and Star like the popcorn!

Read and write the sentences.

Mark was in the marsh

on Thursday. He

spotted a blackbird

on the low tree branch.

There were more birds.

194 **Extended Practice**

Hurl over the Hurdle

Read and write the words.

blur

hurl

short

sharp

blur

purr

curl

snort

harp

Read and write the sentences.

Hurry! Hurl over the hurdle.

Hurry!

Be smart. Don't

jump in the dark.

Read and write the words and sentences.

ark   tore   girl   serve

_____   _____   _____   _____

- - - - -   - - - - -   - - - - -   - - - - -

_____   _____   _____   _____

bark   snore   swirl   swerve

_____   _____   _____   _____

- - - - -   - - - - -   - - - - -   - - - - -

_____   _____   _____   _____

Curt lit the torch.

_____

- -

_____

It will burn

_____

- -

_____

till morning.

_____

- -

_____

Fixing the Walls

Read and write the words. Draw lines to match the words that go together.

fix   _fix_   shelter

tent   mend

king   pile

stack   ruler

candle   rest

sleep   light

Read and write the sentences.

The candle is lit.

Burt tells us a story

of a brave king.

He was the ruler in

a land far from us.

Wet and Dry

Read and write the antonyms.

wet

_ _ _ _ _ wet _ _ _ _ _

dry

_ _ _ _ _ _ _ _ _ _

day

_ _ _ _ _ _ _ _ _ _

night

_ _ _ _ _ _ _ _ _ _

happy

_ _ _ _ _ _ _ _ _ _

sad

_ _ _ _ _ _ _ _ _ _

fat

_ _ _ _ _ _ _ _ _ _

thin

_ _ _ _ _ _ _ _ _ _

under

_ _ _ _ _ _ _ _ _ _

over

_ _ _ _ _ _ _ _ _ _

whisper

_ _ _ _ _ _ _ _ _ _

yell

_ _ _ _ _ _ _ _ _ _

Read and write the antonym pairs.

slow   fast

first   last

sick   well

fresh   stale

stop   go

big   little

Read and write the sentences.

Stop! The stove is hot.

Extended Practice

Balloons

Read and write the words.

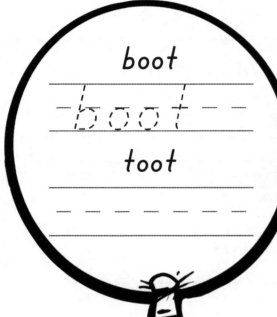

boot
_____
booot
_____
toot
_____
- - - - - - - - -
_____

moon
_____
- - - - - - - - -
_____

soon
_____

room
_____
- - - - - - - - -
_____

broom
_____

loop
_____
- - - - - - - - -
_____

troop
_____
- - - - - - - - -

zoo
_____
- - - - - - - - -

too
_____
- - - - - - - - -

booth
_____
- - - - - - - - -

tooth
_____

Read and write the poem.

I penned a little tune

In the moon in June.

I sang it in my room

As I spun my loom.

I hope you like my tune.

A Loose Goose

Read and write the words.

zoom

zoom

bloom

hoot

root

noon

spoon

pool

cool

Read and write the sentence.

Have you seen

Have

a goose on the loose?

Read and write the words and sentences.

roof   rooftop   roost   rooster

food   seafood   cartoon   teaspoon

Please step on the stool

and grab the tool.

We will fix the pool.

Brooke's Bible

Read and write the rhyming words.

cook

cook

good

wood

brook

hood

stood

Read and write the sentence.

Brooke got a Bible

Brooke

at the bookstore.

Read and write the words and sentences.

book

cookbook

checkbook

foot

footprint

footstool

Brooke went to the shore.

Driftwood washed up

by the sea.

A Look at the Hook

Read and write the sentences.

Pal put a bug on the

Pal

hook. He began to fish.

He sat and he waited.

There was a tug

on the line.

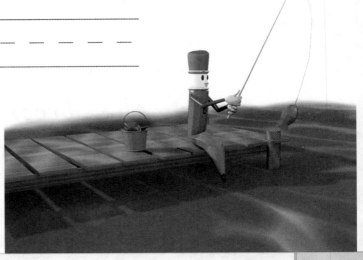

Read and write the words and sentences.

poodle   bamboo   stood

The woodchuck looked

at the woodcutter.

He shook his fur

and ran to the brook.

Extended Practice

Sun or Rain

Read and write each word below the correct heading.

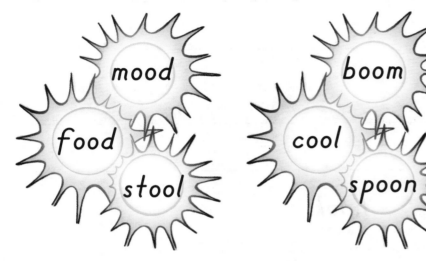

nōon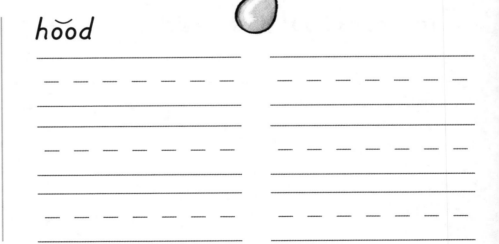

mood

hŏod

Read and write the words and sentences.

carpet

pool

charm

Stan sat on the stool.

purr

cook

hook

The cookbook is red.

Circus Time

Read and write the words. Draw lines to match the words with similar meanings.

pony   *pony*   glad

happy   horse

trotting   mend

fix   running

candy   sweets

Read and write the sentences.

The pony ran in

_____

- - - - - - - - - - - - - - - -

the ring. Two

_____

- - - - - - - - - - - - - - - -

horses trotted inside

_____

- - - - - - - - - - - - - - - -

the circle too.

_____

- - - - - - - - - - - - - - - -

212   **Extended Practice**

Clowns

Read and write the sentences.

The clowns are in town.

The

One clown is upside down.

The sad clown has

a flower.

Read and write the words and sentence.

cow bow how now

plow howl growl towel

down gown town crown

The cowgirl ate

cotton candy.

The Clowns and the Hound

Read and write the sentences.

The clowns bounce and

The

the hound barks.

The crowd shouts.

Write the letters.

b b

k k

h h

Read and write the words. Draw lines to match the words with similar meanings.

class house

~~class house~~

puppy house

plant house

house on water

doghouse

schoolhouse

houseboat

greenhouse

A Gentleman and a Gem

Read and write the words.

gem   germ   gym

gem

Read and write the sentences.

The gentleman gave the lady

The

a ring. It had

a red gemstone.

Read and write the sentences.

Some schoolhouses have

only one room.

Others have many rooms.

My school has a gym.

We play games there.

Roaring with Rage

Read and write the sentences.

A huge tiger is

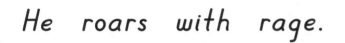

out of his cage.

He roars with rage.

Read and write the words.

age

page

wage

stage

Read and write the sentences.

Did the tiger lunge?

He took a plunge

from the stool.

The crowd began to shout.

He sat down.

Extended Practice

Granny and Cotton Candy

Read and write the words.

candy

candy

clown

gum

grin

cell

race

gem

stage

Read and write the sentences.

Granny likes cotton candy.

Granny

Grace looked in the cage.

The tiger was on the stage.

Read and write the sentences.

Some clowns do cartwheels.

Others clap their hands

and clomp their shoes.

Many clowns with happy

faces sweep the floor.

Clowns on Stage

Read and write the words.

down

large

cage

shower

crowd

brown

age

plunge

howl

tower

huge

gentle

Read and write the sentences.

It was sundown.

The owl hooted.

Big cats in the woods

hid and growled. Moose

sounded like foghorns.

Troy's Toy

Read and write the words.

boy

boy

toy

Troy

coin

join

noise

Read and write the sentences.

Troy had ten coins.

Troy

He got a round toy.

It made a loud pop!

Read and write the words and sentences.

boil

boiled

boiling

joy

enjoy

cowboy

The cowboy had two

coins. He put them

in his pocket.

Extended Practice

Hoe the Soil

Read and write the words.

haven't

~~haven't~~

don't

isn't

I'll

we'll

you'll

Read and write the sentences.

I'll hoe the soil tonight.

~~I'll~~

Then we'll

plant the corn.

Read and write the words and sentences.

mouth   mouse   mound

broil   toil   soil

Some toys are noisy.

Roy's voice is lower

than Troy's.

A Bright Light

Read and write the sentences.

Saul saw a bright

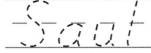

light. A voice asked,

"Why do you hurt Me?"

Saul asked, "Who are You?"

"I am Jesus."

—Bible truth from Acts 9:3–5

Read and write the words and sentences.

jaw   law   paw   saw

fawn   hawk   lawn   yawn

Paul likes to draw horses.

What do you

like to draw?

Extended Practice

Love the Lord

Read and write the sentence.

God wants you

God

to love Him

with all your heart.

—*Bible truth from Deuteronomy 6:5*

Write the letters.

m   m

n   n

Read and write the words and sentence.

ball   call   tall

_____   _____   _____
- - - - - - - - -   - - - - - - - - -   - - - - - - - - -
_____   _____   _____

kickball   meatball   snowball

_____   _____   _____
- - - - - - - - -   - - - - - - - - -   - - - - - - - - -
_____   _____   _____

Roy plays baseball on

_____
- -
_____

Mondays after school.

_____
- -
_____

Days of the Week

Read and write the days of the week.

Sunday

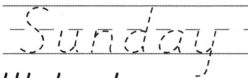

Monday

Tuesday

Wednesday

Thursday

Friday

Saturday

Read and write the sentence.

Sunday is the Lord's day.

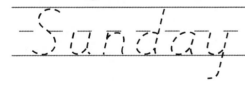

—*Bible truth from Revelation 1:10*

Read and write the sentences.

Nightfall had come.

Jenny sat on the porch.

Where was her pet

rabbit? Thump! Thumper was

under the porch.

Frosting and Sprinkles

Read and write the words.

toss   cross   frost

toss

Read and write the sentences.

It is Steve's birthday.

_It_

Mother is making a cake

with frosting and sprinkles.

Read and write the words and sentence.

boss

loss

moss

long

song

tongs

strong

throng

belong

Buddy barks when the

doorbell ding-dongs.

A Trumpet and a Harp

Read and write the sentences.

I'm a trumpet.

I'm

I am made of brass.

I'm a harp.

Fingers pluck my strings.

Choose a word to complete each sentence. Write the sentence.

book	net	friend	fire

A _____ is for reading.

_____

- - - - - - - - - - - - - - - - - - -

_____

A _____ is for burning.

_____

- - - - - - - - - - - - - - - - - - -

_____

A _____ is for fishing.

_____

- - - - - - - - - - - - - - - - - - -

_____

A _____ is for helping.

_____

- - - - - - - - - - - - - - - - - - -

_____

Extended Practice

Let Us Sing

Read and write the words.

playground   cowboy   room

playground

Read and write the sentences.

Sing to the Lord.

Sing

Sing to Him with joy.

He is like a firm rock.

—Bible truth from Psalm 95:1

Read and write the words and sentence.

age

hinge

wage

singe

stage

fringe

Peggy played her trumpet

on the stage.

The Fiddler

Read and write the words.

fiddle   middle   riddle

fiddle

Read and write the sentences.

This gentleman plays

This

the fiddle well.

The gentleman is tall.

The fiddle looks little.

Read and write the words and sentence.

jiggle

jumble

juggle

ramble

rattle

rumple

dangle

dazzle

drizzle

Nick heard the rumble

of the thunder.

A Drumming Judge

Read and write the words.

judge *judge*

wedge

fudge

ridge

bridge

hedge

badge

lodge

Read and write the sentence.

The judge judges music.

The

Read and write the sentences.

Mick and Midge will

play their trumpets in

the band. They rubbed

off every smudge and

made their trumpets shine.

A Pitch Pipe

Read and write the sentence.

This pitch pipe can

This

give a high pitch

or a low pitch.

Read and write the words.

batch

batch

catch

fetch

sketch

itch

hitch

Read and write the words and sentences.

hatch   match   snatch

_____ _____ _____

- -

_____ _____ _____

stretch   stitch   switch

_____ _____ _____

- -

_____ _____ _____

April mended the hole
_____

- -

_____

with a patch. The
_____

- -

_____

patch did not scratch.
_____

- -

_____

246 **Extended Practice**

God's Riches

Read and write the sentence.

God will supply

everything you need.

—Bible truth from Philippians 4:19

Write the letters.

P   P

r   r

Read and write the sentences.

Sam nudged Dan.

His trumpet was

out of pitch.

Dan fixed the pitch.

Songs of Songbirds

Read and write the words.

lost   songbird   crossroad

lost

Read and write the sentences.

The songbirds came.

The

Winter was gone.

We heard songs of

birds everywhere.

Read and write the words and sentences.

frosty   crossed   longest

_____   _____   _____

- - - - - - - - -   - - - - - - - -   - - - - - - - -

_____   _____   _____

It was a frosty morning.

_____

- -

The flowers looked like

_____

- -

they had a thin coat

_____

- -

of white icing.

_____

- -

_____

A Frog on a Log

Read and write the sentences.

The frog sits on a log.

The

It sings a song.

Write the letters.

v

x

z

Read and write the words and sentence.

moth

cloth

broth

soft

softer

softest

hayloft

dishcloth

softball

A softball is softer

than a baseball.

Jesus Cares for You

Read and write the sentences.

Give all the things you

Give

care for to Jesus. Jesus

cares for you.

—Bible truth from I Peter 5:7

Write the words.

care

care

fair

share

pair

Read and write the words and sentence.

air

stair

chair

glare

scare

snare

Will you share

a pair of hares?

Extended Practice

Mr. Blare

Read and write the words.

telephone

-telephone-

trophy

alphabet

elephant

Read and write the sentence.

Mr. Blare taught

-Mr.-

Jimmy to play the trumpet.

Read and write the words and sentences.

beware   stairway

_____   _____

- - - - - - - - - -   - - - - - - - - - -

_____   _____

Midge marched happily

_____

- -

_____

through the zoo.

_____

- -

_____

She took a photo

_____

- -

_____

of the elephant.

_____

- -

_____

256   **Extended Practice**

Softer and Higher

Read and write the sentences.

Jane's harp sounds softer

Jane's

than Jake's trumpet.

Milly's flute sounds higher

than Carl's horn.

Write the letter.

C   C

Read and write the words and sentences.

dear

near

nearly

large

larger

largest

There was a large

dog near us.

What is the largest dog?

Slowly and Loudly

Read and write the words.

loudly

loudly

softly

brightly

darkly

quietly

slowly

sadly

gladly

quickly

Read and write the sentence.

Curt played his drum loudly.

Curt

Read and write the words and sentences.

gently

gruffly

closely

lightly

gladness

sadness

Deb is friendly to all.

Her sweetness is a blessing.

Flutes

Read and write the words.

basement

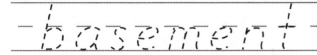

payment

statement

pavement

excitement

settlement

Read and write the sentence.

They played their flutes.

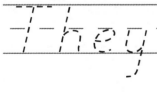

Read and write the words and sentences.

goodness   meekness

_____   _____
- - - - - - - - - - -   - - - - - - - - - - -
_____   _____

Mark heard noises
_____
- -
_____

in the basement.
_____
- -
_____

Carefully he went
_____
- -
_____

downstairs. Meow!
_____
- -
_____

Big, Bigger, Biggest

Read and write the words.

big   bigger  biggest

big

- - - - - - - - - - -   - - - - - - - - - - -

Read and write the sentences.

The drum is bigger than

The

the trumpet. The flute is

the thinnest of the three.

Read the words. Write each group of words in alphabetical order.

a b c d e f g h i j k l m n o p q r s t u v w x y z

king

father

more

love

_____father_____

moss

wage

stair

tool

glad

bright

crown

pain

Making Music

Read and write the sentences. Draw lines to match the sentences with the pictures.

Jane crashed them.

Jane

Pedro strummed it.

Ed is blowing it.

Sue is singing softly.

Write the letter.

S S

Read the words. Write each group of words in alphabetical order.

a b c d e f g h i j k l m n o p q r s t u v w x y z

softer	loudly	shortest
higher	softly	longest
lower	quickly	hardest
faster	badly	tallest

faster

Honk and Bark

Read and write the sentences.

Honk is to goose as

Honk

bark is to dog.

Chimp is to tree as

fish is to sea.

Write the letter.

E   E

Read and write the words and sentences.

hair   chair   rare   spare

_____   _____   _____   _____

- - - - - -   - - - - - -   - - - - - -   - - - - - -

_____   _____   _____   _____

Pants are to legs as

_____

- -

_____

shirt is to arms.

_____

- -

_____

Hat is to hair as

_____

- -

_____

scarf is to neck.

_____

- -

_____

Grain in the Rain

Read and write the sentences.

Water drips

Water

down the drain.

Rain helps to

grow the grain.

Write the letter.

O   O

Read and write the words and sentences.

patch

scare

scarecrow

The scarecrow scares the

crows away. The crows

don't like its

floppy straw hat.

Happiness

Read and write the words.

happy   fair   godly

happy

unhappy   unfair   ungodly

Read and write the sentence.

The people who serve

The

God will be happy.

—*Bible truth from Psalm 144:15*

Read and write the words and sentences.

sleep

_____

_ _ _ _ _ _ _ _ _ _

_____

wake

_____

_ _ _ _ _ _ _ _ _ _

_____

asleep

_____

_ _ _ _ _ _ _ _ _ _

_____

awake

_____

_ _ _ _ _ _ _ _ _ _

_____

My cat is asleep. The

_____

_ _

_____

kittens are all awake!

_____

_ _

_____

Children's Church

Read and write the sentences.

Rose sang alone

Rose

at children's church.

Dave recited a verse.

Ann played her flute.

Read and write the words and sentence.

untie

untwist

unzip

unbend

unlace

unlock

Sam unzipped his jacket.

Softball

Read and write the words.

don't

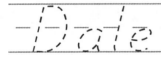

do not

doesn't

does not

Read and write the sentences.

Dale and Jack play softball.

Dale

They toss and bat the ball.

Read and write the words and sentence.

replay

refill

refresh

---

unpack

unplug

unsnap

Tom will unlatch the gate.

Sounds of Music

Read and write the words.

beside

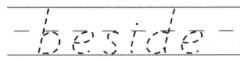

before

_____
_____

uncoil

_____
_____

unpin

_____
_____

below

_____
_____

unlikely

_____
_____

Read and write the sentences.

Sit beside me.

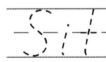

_____
_____

I will play before you.

_____
_____

Read and write the words and sentences.

unbend

repair

rewire

----

return

recite

replace

My kite came apart.

Dad can repair it.

Airports and Airplanes

Read and write the sentences.

Airports have many airplanes

Airports

and jets. Some carry

people. Others carry mail.

Read and write the words and sentence.

fare   farewell   stairway

_____   _____   _____

- - - - - - - -   - - - - - - - - - -   - - - - - - - -

_____   _____   _____

stare   wheelchair   airmail

_____   _____   _____

- - - - - - - -   - - - - - - - - - -   - - - - - - - - -

_____   _____   _____

The stairway took them

_____

- -

_____

to the airplane.

_____

- -

_____

A Piece of Cake

Read and write the words.

chief

field

niece

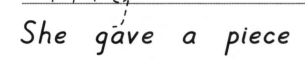

Read and write the sentences.

My niece baked a cake.

She gave a piece

to Luke and Kate.

Read and write the words and sentence.

piece

shield

cookie

shriek

The sun is shining

on the windshield.

Cuts and Drives

Read and write the words.

cub

cut

drop

drive

cub

cube

cute

grab

grade

Read and write the sentences.

Mr. Kind cuts the grass.

_Mr._

Mr. Pane drives a boat.

Read and write the words and sentences.

grass   let   mop

_____   _____   _____

- - - - -   - - - - -   - - - - -

_____   _____   _____

graze   leap   mole

_____   _____   _____

- - - - -   - - - - -   - - - - -

_____   _____   _____

The pail fell in the lake.

_____

- -

_____

The hat fell in the tub.

_____

- -

_____

Bunnies and Daisies

Read and write the words. Draw lines to match the words with the pictures.

bunny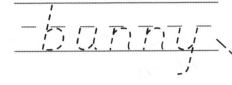

 bunnies

baby

 babies

penny

 pennies

kitty

kitties

daisy

  daisies

Read and write the words and sentences.

empty   empties   emptied

_____   _____   _____

- - - - - - - - -   - - - - - - - - -   - - - - - - - - -

_____   _____   _____

try   tries   tried

_____   _____   _____

- - - - - - - - -   - - - - - - - - -   - - - - - - - - -

_____   _____   _____

hurry   hurries   hurried

_____   _____   _____

- - - - - - - - -   - - - - - - - - -   - - - - - - - - -

_____   _____   _____

Billy emptied the trash. He

_____

- -

_____

hurried to dress for school.

_____

- -

_____

Fred and Ted

Read and write the words.

head   read   bread   thread

head _ _ _ _ _ _ _ _ _ _ _ _ _ _ _

Read and write the sentences. Circle the words that rhyme with *spread*.

Fred ate some bread.

Fred _ _ _ _ _ _ _ _ _ _ _ _

Ted hit his head.

_ _ _ _ _ _ _ _ _ _ _ _ _ _ _ _

Write the letters.

F *F*

T *T*

Read and write the words and sentences.

headlight   arrowhead

_____   _____
- - - - - - - - - - - -   - - - - - - - - - - - -
_____   _____

headlines   overhead

_____   _____
- - - - - - - - - - - -   - - - - - - - - - - - -
_____   _____

We are ready to race.

_____
- -
_____

Buddy gets a head start.

_____
- -
_____

Be Kind

Read and write the sentence.

Be kind to each other,

Be

love each other, and

forgive each other.

—Bible truth from Ephesians 4:32

Read and write the words.

kind

kind

kindly

kindness

Read and write the sentences. Circle the long *i* words.

Find your backpack.

Be kind to your sister.

Mind your manners.

Rewind the string.

Unwind the garden hose.

Pets

Read and write the words.

gold

gold

molt

toll

jolt

cold

colt

poll

scroll

Read and write the sentences.

Henry has a colt.

Henry

Beth has a goldfish.

Read and write the words and sentence.

unfold

unroll

untold

folded

rolled

told

Mom told me to unroll

the sleeping bags.

Chalk Talk

Read and write the words.

talk   stalk   calf   half

talk

Read and write the compound words.

chalkboard   sidewalk

chalkboard

Read and write the sentences.

Kay's chalk broke in half.

Kay's

Ben talks to his calf.

Read and write the poem, following your teacher's directions.

Dress Up

You will put on
A yellow crown,
A purple cape,
A big red ring,
And be the king!

I will put on
A bright blue gown,
A small pink purse,
A stone that's green,
And be the queen!

—L. Michelle Rosier

Trust God

Read and write the sentence.

The Bible teaches me

The

to trust in God

and not be

afraid of people.

—Bible truth from Psalm 56:11

Read and write the words. Match words to make compound words.

wrist

wreck

ship

band

hand

writing

Read and write the sentence.

Alex and Ashley are twins.

Treasures

Read and write the sentences.

Nick has a pocketknife.

- - - Nick - - - - - - - - - - - - - - -

Nancy has a backpack.

Mark has an old wrench.

Milly has a wreath.

Read and write the poem, following your teacher's directions.

Far Blue Star

Faraway star,
As blue as ice,
How can you know
I think you're nice?

Faraway star,
As blue as blue,
How can I know
You like me too?

—Louise D. Nicholas

**Extended
Practice**

Amazing Grace

Read and write the lines from "Amazing Grace."

Amazing grace!

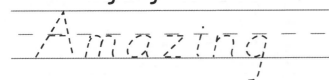

How sweet the sound, That

saved a wretch like me!

Write the letters.

Read and write the sentences.

God shows love to sinners.

_____

- -

_____

You cannot work for

_____

- -

_____

God's love or grace.

_____

- -

_____

God's grace saves sinners.

_____

- -

_____

—*Bible truth from Ephesians 2:8–9*

Mew and Dew

Read and write the sentences.

Mew, the kitten,

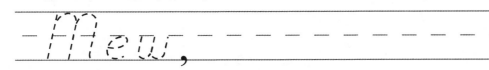

shook his paw.

Mew's paws were

wet from the dew.

Read and write the words.

new	pew	grew	threw
new			

Read and write the words and sentences.

new   newcomer   newscast

_____   _____   _____
- - - - - - - -   - - - - - - - -   - - - - - - - -
_____   _____   _____

Drew blew and he blew.
_____
- -
_____

He blew out all of
_____
- -
_____

the candles on
_____
- -
_____

the yellow cake.
_____
- -
_____

302   **Extended Practice**

King of the Jews

Read and write the sentence.

The wise men asked, "Where

The

is the man who was born

to be King of the Jews?"

—Bible truth from Matthew 2:1–2

Read and write the words.

few

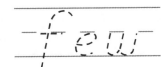

nephew

jewel

Read and write the words and sentences.

crew

drew

renew

What is Paul drawing? He

draws ships. This ship is

gray and has huge guns on

deck. It is a battleship.

Extended Practice

A Special Print

_____
- - - - - - - - - - - - - - - - -
_____

Read and write the phrases.

Pam's comb

Brent's thumb

Pam's

Rob's thumbprint

Write the letters.

P   P

B   B

R   R

Read and write the words and sentences.

numb   number   plum   plumber

The newscast was about

children playing baseball.

The teams played

every Saturday.

The Batter

Read and write the words.

batter

banner

drummer

dragging

flapping

trotting

Read and write the sentences.

The batter lightly

The

hit the ball.

Then he ran.

Read and write the words and sentences.

muddy

peppy

puppy

fluffy

floppy

bunny

The white bunny was

frisky. He hopped

under the shed.

Farm Animals

Read and write the sentences. Circle the contractions.

Let's go to the farm.

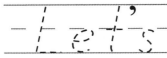

That's a lamb.

It's a calf.

That's a hog.

Read and write the words and sentence.

goat

snake

pig

cow

duck

hen

The newborn goat

had no horns.

Extended Practice

Bread and Jelly

Read and write the sentence. Circle the naming words.

Vick and Patty sat in

Vick

the field and ate

bread and jelly.

Write the letters.

X   X

V   V

Read and write the words and sentences.

Peter

Reggie

Rusty

Peggy

Deb

Barb

Becky swims in the pond.

Reggie fishes in the pond.

The Only God

Read and write the sentence.

Our God is

Our

the only God.

—*Bible truth from Isaiah 45:21*

Read and write the words.

Luke

Luke

James

Mark

Cain

Peter

Eve

Read and write the words and sentences.

carport

bagpipe

skipping

jumper

kitties

carpet

Matt looked. The fishhook

was gone. He netted

a large fish.

Extended Practice

A Poem

Read and write the poem, following your teacher's directions.

Raindrops

Drip.
Drip.
Drop.
Rain falls on top
Of my bright yellow hat.

Drop.
Drop.
Drip.
And raindrops slip
Off my wet orange cat.

—Robin E. Scroggins

Read and write the words and sentence.

slip   slap   slam

_____   _____   _____

– – – – – – – –   – – – – – – – –   – – – – – – – –

_____   _____   _____

trip   trap   trot

_____   _____   _____

– – – – – – – –   – – – – – – – –   – – – – – – – –

_____   _____   _____

The raindrops fell

_____

– –

_____

on the window.

_____

– –

_____

A Poem

Read and write the poem, following your teacher's directions.

Fishing

My bait for the day
Is a blue-green bug.
I wait by the pond
For a tug, tug, tug.

I stay by the pond
With my pole and bait.
I lean on a tree
And I wait, wait, wait.

I dream by the pond
Of a ten-inch fish.
I sleep by the pond
As I wish, wish, wish.

—Jan Joss

Read and write the words and sentence.

my

dry

drying

try

fly

flown

We sat quietly in

the boat waiting

to catch a fish.

Extended Practice

Walk or Ride

Read and write the words.

climb   cry   write

climb

Read and write the sentences. Circle the action words.

Joy and Jill (walk) to school.

Joy

Jay rides a bus.

Write the letters.

J   J

y   y

Read and write the names. Begin each name with a capital letter.

Boys	Girls	Pets
Abe	Ashley	Buddy
Karl	Brooke	Loro
Gill	Jenny	Birdie
Troy	Liz	Muffin

Colors of the Animals

Read and write the animal names. Choose a color you like for each animal. Write it in the space.

black   brown   pink   red   white   gray   green   yellow

pig

pig

pony

sheep

dog

frog

cat

bird

fish

Read and write the words.

backpack

basketball

clubhouse

seashore

spaceship

windmill

Draw a picture of one of the items you like.

Which Is First?

Read the words. For each pair of words, write the word that comes first in alphabetical order.

a b c d e f g h i j k l m n o p q r s t u v w x y z

desk
dust

desk

candy
chalk

book
brick

knife
kitty

apple
art

flag
foot

jump
jam

swing
slide

wet
water

Read and write the poem, following your teacher's directions.

Tell Me, Yellow

Tell me, Yellow,
Is it fun
To be the color
Of the sun?

Tell me, Yellow,
If you know,
How God made
Your color so.

—Elizabeth Smith

Vocabulary

Read and write the sentences.

A wren is a small bird.

A

A limb is a tree branch.

A thief is one who steals.

A knee is part of a leg.

Read and write the sentences.

A knapsack is like a

backpack. A bugle is one

kind of horn. A corner is

where two ends meet. An

otter is a water animal.

Which Is Which?

Read the words. Write each word under the correct heading.

Kim	*wildcat*	*fish*
colt	*knee*	*forehead*
wrist	*Will*	*Peggy*

Animals

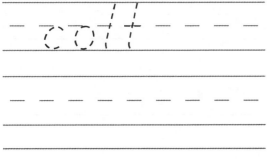

Names

Parts of the Body

Write the letters.

   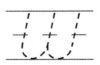

Read and write the words and sentences.

shirt   shark   thumb

_____   _____   _____

- - - - - - - -   - - - - - - - -   - - - - - - - -

_____   _____   _____

whiz   chick   chest

_____   _____   _____

- - - - - - - -   - - - - - - - -   - - - - - - - -

_____   _____   _____

Those plants are thorny.

_____

- -

_____

Mark is a friendly chap.

_____

- -

_____

A Poem

Read and write the poem, following your teacher's directions.

My Frog

I had a frog, big and green.
One day he made my sister scream.

We took a ride in Mother's car.
The lid, it slid right off his jar.

Said Mom, "All frogs must stay outside."
I think my sis is on her side!

—Linda O. Parker

Read and write the poem.

Green

The grass blades bend. Look!

Leaves sway. Look!

Frogs hop on pads. Look!

All of these are green.